STINGRAY

...STAND BY FOR ACTION

**Edited and compiled by
Alan Fennell**

RAVETTE BOOKS

© 1992 ITC Entertainment Group Ltd.
Licensed by Copyright Promotions Ltd.

Written, edited and compiled by Alan Fennell.

Artwork by Ronald Embleton and Steve Kyte.

Photographs by Martin Bower.

First published by Ravette Books Limited 1992.

Printed and bound for Ravette Books Limited
3 Glenside Estate, Star Road,
Partridge Green, Horsham,
West Sussex RH13 8RA
An Egmont Company
by Proost International Bookproduction, Belgium

ISBN: 1 85304 457 1

Contents

STAND BY FOR ACTION...

STINGRAY

THE WORLD IS AT PEACE... BUT THE NEED FOR WARSHIPS AND STRIKE AIRCRAFT STILL EXISTS...

AN HOUR LATER AT MARINEVILLE...

THAT'S THE SECOND AIRCRAFT CARRIER IN A MONTH.

A VESSEL THAT SIZE CAN'T JUST DISAPPEAR WITHOUT TRACE...

ON THE ISLAND THE SINISTER X20 IS AT WORK...

I HAVE SIGHTED ANOTHER CARRIER, MIGHTY TITAN... STINGRAY IS ESCORTING IT.

IN THE UNDERWATER CITY OF TITANICA, TITAN ISSUES HIS ORDERS.

GOOD! IN ADDITION TO ADDING TO MY FLEET THIS COULD BE MY CHANCE TO KILL TROY TEMPEST!

LAUNCH MECHANICAL FISH SEVEN. DESTROY STINGRAY OR DIE!

FIRE STING MISSILE!

TROY... IT'S A MECHANICAL FISH!

STAND BY TO FIRE STING MISSILE!

LOOK!

EYES TURN AS AN ENORMOUS JELLYFISH LEAPS ABOVE THE SUBMARINE AIRCRAFT CARRIER...

BUT TWO OF THEM HAVE, CAPTAIN— AND A THIRD IS SHORTLY DUE TO SAIL... YOU WILL ESCORT HER IN STINGRAY.

APPROACHING ISLAND OF LEMOY!

STINGRAY

TWO HOURS LATER...

I'M PICKING UP A STRANGE ECHO ON THE SOUND SCAN, TROY.

OK, PHONES... BLOW ONE... LET'S TAKE A LOOK BELOW.

IT'S SOMETHING PRETTY BIG... AND IT'S HEADING OUR WAY... FAST!

STINGRAY

MEANWHILE, IN THE PATH OF THE CARRIER, THE GIGANTIC JELLYFISH RISES FROM THE DEPTHS.

5

STAND BY FOR ACTION...

STINGRAY

TWO GIANT CARRIERS HAVE MYSTERIOUSLY DISAPPEARED. STINGRAY ESCORTS A THIRD SHIP, BUT BECOMES INVOLVED IN AN UNDERSEA BATTLE. MEANWHILE, ON THE SURFACE...

STINGRAY RACES TO THE AREA...

SHE'S GOING DOWN INTO REAL DEEP WATERS.

KEEP AFTER HER, PHONES... WE'VE GOTTA FIND OUT WHAT'S CAUSED HER TO DIVE.

SUDDENLY...

THE INTENSIVE SEARCH BEGINS IN THE AIR...

...AND UNDER THE WAVES...

THE SUPER SUB ERUPTS FROM THE SEA...

DESPITE ITS GIGANTIC SIZE THE JELLYFISH CLOSES WITH FANTASTIC SPEED.

THE SOUNDSCAN INDICATES THAT THE CARRIER IS DIVING, TROY.

THE CARRIER'S CREW REMAIN SILENT...

WE KNOW SHE'S A SUBMARINE VESSEL, PHONES, BUT WHY HAVEN'T THEY CLEARED THEIR ACTION BY RADIO?

...STING ...LES!

I GUESS WE DON'T HAVE TO WORRY ABOUT THAT ONE, TROY.

RECKON NOT...BUT NOW WE'VE LOST THE CARRIER, TELL MARINEVILLE TO SCRAMBLE SEARCH AIRCRAFT!

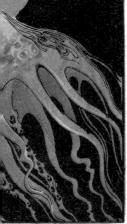

TROY...THERE'S A JELLYFISH MOVING IN BEHIND US...IT MUST BE TWO MILES ACROSS!

WHAT! LET'S GET OUTTA HERE!

TROY BOOSTS STINGRAY TO RATE SIX...

STINGRAY

IT'S GOT US, PHONES...WE'RE DONE FOR!

STAND BY FOR ACTION...

STINGRAY

THREE GIANT AIRCRAFT CARR HAVE DISAPPEA THEN STINGRAY, INVESTIGATING, IS ENVELOPED A MONSTER JELLYFISH — AN DRAGGED TO TH DEPTHS OF THE OCEAN.

THE JELLYFISH, TROY... IT'S LEAVING.

YEH... WE'RE IN SOME KINDA ARTIFICIAL CAVERN UNDER THE SEA.

THE WATER'S BEING PUMPED OUT...

TROY... LOOK OVER THERE!

THE MISSING CARRIERS!

IT'S BEEN TWO HOURS, FATHER... WHAT COULD HAVE HAPPENED TO STINGRAY?

I DON'T LIKE IT, ATLANTA... PREPARE HYDROMIC MISSILES FOR LAUNCH... SOUND BATTLE STATIONS!

MISSILES STANDING BY!

MEANWHILE, BENEA THE OCEAN...

THE CARRIER CREWMAN...THEY'R OKAY, TROY... LOOK, THEY'RE ON THE DECKS.

HE CAN'T HEAR ME, PHONES... HE'S IN A TRANCE... THEY ALL ARE!

SUDDENLY VIVI BATHE TROY AN

8

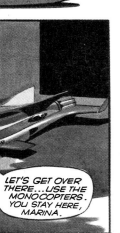

STAND BY FOR ACTION...

STINGRAY

INVESTIGATING THE DISAPPEARANCES OF THREE GIANT AIRCRAFT CARRIERS, STINGRAY IS ENVELOPED BY A MONSTER JELLYFISH AND TAKEN TO A STRANGE UNDERSEA CAVERN. THEN RAYS OF BRIGHT LIGHT PARALYSE TROY AND PHONES.

NOT FAR AWAY IS TITANICA...

THANKS TO MARINA... BUT WHY ISN'T SHE AFFECTED?

SHE'S FROM UNDER THE SEA, PHONES... HER MOLECULAR STRUCTURE IS DIFFERENT FROM OURS. COME ON, LET'S GET BACK TO STINGRAY.

THE RAYS WON'T PENETRATE STINGRAY'S HULL...?

NO, PHONES... OKAY, MARINA... WE'RE SAFE...

IT IS UNFORTUNATE, BUT IT CANNOT BE HELPED. PROCEED WITH MY PLAN... I WILL DEAL WITH TEMPEST AND HIS CREW LATER.

IN THE CAVERN...

IT'S FLOODING AGAIN, TROY...

STINGRAY

THIS COULD BE OUR CHANCE TO ESCAPE...

SUDDENLY...

IT'S NO GOOD, TROY... WE'RE TRAPPED.

STINGRAY

STAND BY FOR ACTION...

STINGRAY

TITAN, EVIL RULER OF AN UNDERSEA RACE OF STRANGE PEOPLE, HAS CAPTURED AND HYPNOTISED THE CREWS OF THREE GIANT SUBMARINE AIRCRAFT CARRIERS BELONGING TO THE WORLD NAVY...

TITAN'S PURPO... DESTROY MAR... BY USING THE... ALLIED WAR S...

MEANWHILE, STINGRAY IS TRAPPED IN AN UNDERSEA CAVERN...A MONSTER JELLYFISH STANDING GUARD.

WE'VE GOTTA GET OUT OF THIS... BUT IF WE MOVE, THAT OVERGROWN MUTATION WILL POUNCE AGAIN.

WHAT'S WRONG, MARINA?

I GUESS SHE'S SEEN SOMETHING OUT THERE...

SO, TROY ... I HAVE YOU ... SOON, THE ... WHOSE GR... ACCELERAT... SCIENTISTS ... YOU ...

BEFOR... ANSWE...

TRACKING STATIONS TO CONTROL TOWER... MISSING CARRIERS HAVE BEEN SIGHTED OFF COAST. THEY ARE INTACT AND APPEAR TO BE SAFE.

GREAT! ANY WORD FROM STINGRAY?

WE'RE UNDER FIRE... SOUND BATTLE STATIONS!

THE ENTIRE BASE BEGINS TO SINK INTO THE GROUND.

AS THE STEE... CONCRETE C... CLOSE OVER... BASE, THE INS... ABOVE ARE ...

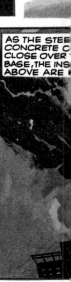

STAND BY FOR ACTION...

STINGRAY

TITAN HAS HYPNOTISED WORLD NAVY FLIERS TO ATTACK MARINEVILLE...

MEANWHILE, STINGRAY IS TRAPPED IN AN UNDERSEA CAVERN.

NOW MY PET JELLYFISH WILL BRING YOU TO TITANICA... AND I WILL HAVE THE PLEASURE OF DESTROYING YOU ALL.

HANG ON, TROY... HERE COMES THAT OVERGROWN JELLYFISH AGAIN !

THE TITAN-INSP MUTATION STIRS

FIRE STING MISSILES !

IT'S TOUGH AIR-FILLED JELLY SAC PENETRATED BY THE LETHAL STING MISSILES, THE GIANT ORGANISM DIES...

STINGRAY IS STILL IN TITAN'S CAVERN...

THOSE RAYS... THEY'RE STILL ON. IF WE DESTROY THEIR SOURCE WE COULD BREAK THE TRANCE THOSE NAVY GUYS ARE IN.

A STING MISSILE SINGS ITS SONG OF DESTRUCTION...

FOR THE MOMENT, THE MAIN INSTALLATIONS ARE SAFE IN THEIR UNDERGROUND POSITIONS...

BUT IN THE CONTROL TOWER, ANXIETY GROWS.

INTERCEPTOR MISSILES STANDING BY!

PREPARE TO FIRE!

NO, FATHER — THOSE BOYS ARE OUR OWN MEN, WE CAN'T JUST KILL THEM... GIVE THEM A FEW MORE MINUTES, MAYBE THEY'LL CALL OFF THE ATTACK.

TROY LEANS FORWARD EAGERLY... THE JELLYFISH HAS MADE A MISTAKE...

THE STING MISSILE TUBES ARE IN LINE WITH THE CREATURE...

STAND BY, PHONES — WE'VE GOT OUR FIRST CHANCE TO SETTLE THIS ONCE AND FOR ALL.

THE HYPNOTISED COMMANDER OF THE WAR SHIPS CARRIES OUT TITAN'S RELAYED ORDERS.

TITAN SEETHES IN HIS PALACE AT TITANICA.

A THOUSAND MARINE CURSES ON TEMPEST! FOR THIS THE AIR ATTACK ON MARINEVILLE WILL BE INTENSIFIED!

THE EXPLOSIONS ARE TOO POWERFUL.

STAND BY FOR ACTION...

STINGRAY

MARINEVILLE IS UNDER HEAVY ATTACK FROM WORLD NAVY AIRCRAFT WHOSE PILOTS HAVE BEEN HYPNOTISED BY TITAN. IN AN UNDERSEA CAVERN, STINGRAY DESTROYS THE HYPNOSIS INDUCING RAYS, BUT THE WHOLE PLACE COLLAPSES.

STRIKE AIRCRAFT SWOOP IN OVER MARINEVILLE...

WHAT AM I DOING? THAT'S MARINEVILLE DOWN THERE!

OUT OF RADIO CONTACT, THE STINGRAY CREW DO NOT KNOW THEY HAVE SUCCEEDED IN BREAKING TITAN'S SPELL OVER THE NAVY FLIERS.

TROY...WE'LL BE CRUSHED!

ACCELERATION RATE SIX... EMERGENCY!!

STINGRAY RACES TO THE SURFACE...

THE SUPER SUB LOCATES THE THREE AIRCRAFT CARRIERS...

STINGRAY TO COMMANDER TRACEY...ARE YOU RECOVERED?

YES, THANK CAPTAIN TEM BUT WHAT HAPPENED

TELL YOU LATER...DON'T WORRY, I'LL SQUARE THINGS WITH MARINEVILLE.

HANG ON, MARINA... PHONES... HANG ON!

THE THREE AIRCRAFT CARRIERS MOVE TOWARDS THE MARINEVILLE COAST...

WHAT'S GOING ON? I CAN'T REMEMBER SETTING THIS COURSE...

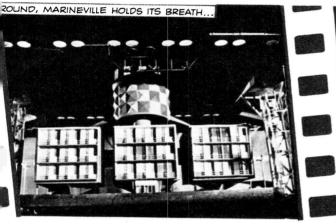

...ROUND, MARINEVILLE HOLDS ITS BREATH...

FATHER... THE AIRCRAFT ARE LEAVING... THE ATTACK'S OVER.

FLIGHT LEADER TO MARINEVILLE TOWER... SORRY, COMMANDER... I DON'T UNDERSTAND THIS.

RETURN TO YOUR CARRIER AT ONCE... ALL CARRIER AIRCRAFT WILL BE GROUNDED PENDING A FULL INVESTIGATION.

AT NIGHTFALL STINGRAY RETURNS TO BASE...

SO YOU SEE, SIR, TITAN WAS BEHIND THE WHOLE ATTACK. WAS THERE MUCH DAMAGE?

SOME, TROY, BUT WE CAN FIX IT. I'M GLAD YOU MADE IT BACK OKAY... YOU DID A SWELL JOB.

ONE PERSON DOESN'T THINK SO...

CURSE TEMPEST... ONE DAY I'LL DESTROY HIM! AS SURE AS I SHALL RULE THE TERRAIN, I SHALL SEE HIM DIE... CURSE HIM!

THE END

STINGRAY IN ACTION

The Wasp's most effective patrol/combat security vessel, this revolutionary undersea craft has a top speed of 600 knots and the power to dive safely to depths never before envisaged by marine engineers.

STAND BY FOR ACTION...

STINGRAY

A GIANT FIREFLASH AIRLINER SCREAMS OVER THE DENSE SOUTH AMERICAN JUNGLE.

WE MUST TAKE NO CHANCES. OUR COASTAL BASE IS AT STAKE.

THE AREA WILL SOON BE READY TO RECEIVE US — ONCE WE HAVE DESTROYED THE MAJOR CITIES ON THE LAND.

THEN WE WILL GROUP OUR FORCES AND RULE THE WHOLE WORLD IN THE NAME OF THE UNDERSEA PEOPLES.

AN UNEARTHLY CLAW OPERATES A FIRING BUTTON...

MARINEVILLE, TWO DAYS LATER...

WE NOW HAVE A FULL REPORT, SHORE. THE NATIVES SAY THEY'VE BEEN TERRORISED BY STRANGE CREATURES...

YES, IT APPEARS THEY COME FROM THE LAKE IN THE HEART OF THE JUNGLE... AND THE WATER HAS TURNED FROM FRESH TO SALT.

SOUNDS LIKE A JOB FOR THE WASPS!

WHILE THE CONFEREN IS IN PROGRESS...

IN THE MIDST OF THE TANGLED UNDERGROWTH LIES A LAKE...

ALIENS ARE PRESENT...

INSIDE THE LOBOT, CRUSTAVONS RECEIVE THE VIBRATIONS CAUSED BY THE AIRLINER'S PROGRESS THROUGH THE AIR.

DID THE TERRAINEAN AIRCRAFT SEE US?

DEAD

THE CRUSTAVONS ARE SATISFIED...

...AND PHONES ...A MISSION...

THAT'S RIGHT, PHONES... NO SURVIVORS... THE AIRLINER HAD BEEN SHOT DOWN...

COMMANDER SHORE'S AT H.Q. NOW...

WASHINGTON D.C.

CRAWLING ON ITS MECHANICAL LEGS, THE LOBOT SEEKS OUT FRESH PREY...

STAND BY FOR ACTION...

STINGRAY

THE LOBOT, STRANGE CRAFT OF THE UNDERSEA CREATURES KNOWN AS CRUSTAVONS, ATTACKS A NATIVE VILLAGE DEEP IN THE JUNGLE

LAUNCH STATIONS ARE SO[...]

WHAT DO YOU THINK WE'LL FIND IN THAT JUNGLE, TROY?

I DON'T KNOW, PHONES... THE DRILL IS FOR US TO GO BY SEA TO THE RENDEZVOUS POINT WHERE THE ARMY WILL TRANSPORT US TO THE LAKE.

AN AIR-LIFT WOULD BE FASTER.

SURE... BUT THE JUNGLE'S TOO DENSE TO MAKE A LANDING ANYWHERE NEAR THE AREA.

TROY FOLLOWS ORDERS...

RENDEZVOUS POINT 29

U.S. ARMY

STINGRAY IS WINCHED ABOARD...

ONCE ABOARD, STINGRAY [...] THE ARMY MACHINE'S CO[...]

SORR[...] LATE, TR[...] TO PUT [...] BLAZIN[...] VILLA[...]

N RETURNS TO THE WATER LAKE...

SOON THE ENTIRE REGION WILL BE CLEAR OF THE PRIMITIVE TERRAINEANS.

THEN OUR JUNGLE BASE CAN BEGIN TO OPERATE.

TROY'S APARTMENT, MARINEVILLE...

SEABORNE, COMMANDER...

OKAY, TROY, SURFACE AND PROCEED TO RENDEZVOUS POINT TWENTY-NINE.

THEY SHOULD HAVE BEEN HERE TO MEET US.

YEAH... MAYBE THE JUNGLE SLOWED THEM DOWN.

WAIT THE MY.

LOOK, PHONES... HERE THEY COME. NOTHING COULD SLOW THAT MACHINE!

ER

MORE DESTRUCTION, EH, MAJOR? LET'S HOPE WE CAN DISCOVER THE CAUSE OF THESE SENSELESS ATTACKS.

HANG ON, FOLKS... HERE WE GO.

THE WEIRD AND WONDERFUL MACHINE TEARS ITS WAY ONWARDS...

U.S. ARMY

BUT THE LOBOT IS AT THAT MOMENT RETURNING TO THE TERRAIN.

STAND BY FOR ACTION...

STINGRAY

BUT THE HUGE MACHINE HARDLY FALTERS IN ITS PROGRESS...

HEY! WE'RE OKAY!

U.S. ARMY

SURE! IT'LL TAKE MORE THAN A FORCE FIVE MISSILE TO STOP THIS BABY.

FIRING GROUND TO GROUND PROJECTILE...

THE SOLDIER DOES NOT MISS A SECOND TIME...

A QUICK EXAMINATION OF THE WRECKAGE AND TROY REACHES CONCLUSIONS...

NO SURVIVORS, TROY...

JUDGING BY THIS PRESSURE GAUGE, THIS CRAFT WAS AMPHIBIOUS.

HMM! LET'S GET TO THAT LAKE.

THERE SH... TROY... DO W... STINGR...

AN HOUR PASSES...

WHEN THE RIPPLES CEASE TO RUFFLE THE LAKE'S SURFACE...

OKAY, MAJOR... I GUESS STINGRAY TAKES OVER FROM HERE.

U.S.

25

STAND BY FOR ACTION...

STINGRAY

CRUSTAVONS, STRANGE UNDERSEA CREATURES, ARE PLANNING TO TAKE OVER THE LAND. STINGRAY IS RUSHED TO A LAKE IN THE BRAZILIAN JUNGLE AND SUBMERGES, FOLLOWING THE ALIEN CRAFT...

THESE ROCK WALLS HAVE BEEN WORKED BY MACHINES, TROY.

YES, PHONES... THOSE CREATURES HAVE TUNNELLED THEIR WAY THROUGH TO THE BED OF THE LAKE.

SLOW DOWN, PHONES... I CAN SEE LIGHTS AHEAD.

YEAH... IT'S A C... ON THE ... BED.

THE TUNNEL LEADS TO THE ATLANTIC OCEAN...

THE LOBOT INCREASES SPEED...

PHO... CAR... ORD...

THE CITY SEEMS TO HAVE NO WARNING SYSTEMS...

THE CRAFT WE WERE FOLLOWING MUST HAVE GONE INSIDE, TROY.

STINGRAY PASSES A WINDOW...

LOOKS LIKE SOME KINDA CONFERENCE GOING ON IN THERE.

I'M GOING TO SWIM UP TO THE WINDOW, PHONES... TAKE STINGRAY AWAY A PIECE AND WAIT ON THE OCEAN FLOOR.

PHONES... I CAN HEAR THEM THROUGH THE GLASS, BUT I DON'T UNDERSTAND THE LANGUAGE. MAYBE MARINA CAN HELP. SEND HER ACROSS.

MOMENTS LATER...

TEN MINUTES LATER...

THE TUNNEL BENDS, THEN GOES STRAIGHT.

OKAY, GUESS WE'VE GOTTA KEEP AFTER THAT CRAFT.

TAKE HER IN CLOSER, PHONES... WE'LL TAKE A LOOK ROUND.

AND ONCE ON THE OCEAN BED PHONES OPERATES A CONTROL AND A HATCH OPENS...

SOON MARINA IS BESIDE TROY...

CAN YOU MAKE OUT WHAT THEY'RE SAYING, MARINA?

AS MARINA NODS HER BEAUTIFUL HEAD...

...TROY TEMPEST IS DISCOVERED...

STAND BY FOR ACTION...

STINGRAY

Stingray follows a hostile alien craft to an undersea city. Troy Tempest and Marina listen in on a conference between the evil Crustavons. Then . . .

QUICK, MARINA... WE'VE BEEN SPOTTED. BACK TO STINGRAY!

INSTAN CRAFT

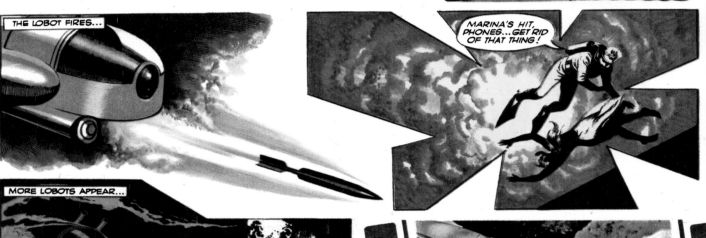

THE LOBOT FIRES...

MORE LOBOTS APPEAR...

MARINA'S HIT, PHONES... GET RID OF THAT THING!

PHONES OPERATES MORE MISSILES...

THE CITY DISINTEGRATES...

STINGRAY'S MOTORS CARRY IT CLEAR OF THE DEVASTATION...

BUT, TROY CAN SHE? M CAN'T SPE

GUESS YOU WERE ONLY WINDED, EH, MARINA? CAN YOU TELL ME WHAT THOSE CREATURES WERE SAYING IN THAT CONFERENCE ROOM?

MARINA — TROY... HURRY! INTO THE HATCH!

THE STING MISSILE SEEKS OUT ITS QUARRY...

DY HELPS MARINA ABOARD...

I'M TAKING NO CHANCES. DESTROY THAT CITY, PHONES!

DEADLY STING MISSILES FLASH FROM STINGRAY...

MEANWHILE, IN A BASE BENEATH THE BRAZILIAN JUNGLE...

I CANNOT GET THROUGH TO OUR CITY.

THEN WE MUST CARRY OUT OUR ORDERS.

WE MUST DESTROY EVERY MAJOR CITY ON EARTH!!

STINGRAY

Not knowing that Stingray has destroyed their undersea city, Crustavons in a secret base beneath the Brazilian jungle prepare to launch missiles at every major capital . . .

GUIDED ROCKET PLANE TWO—SEVEN—ZERO—GREEN—TWELVE . . .

INSTALLATIONS BREAKING SURFACE . . .

PART OF THE DENSE JUNGLE OPENS.

THE HUGE ROCKET STREAKS ACROSS THE ATLANTIC OCEAN AT EIGHTEEN THOUSAND MILES PER HOUR . . . AND REACHES PARIS!

AS PARIS BURNS, STINGRAY SPEEDS BACK ALONG THE TUNNEL THAT LEADS TO THE BRAZILIAN LAKE . . .

THEN MARINA'S PENCIL MAKES ANOTHER MARK . . .

PARIS

FRANCE

YOU'VE CROSSED OUT PARIS . . . DOES THAT MEAN . . . IT'S DESTROYED? BUT HOW?

MARINA'S FI POINTS TO O SPOT ON THE AND TAPS IT INSISTANTLY.

SOON STINGRAY IS LIFTED FROM THE SHALLOW EDGE OF THE LAKE . . .

US ARMY

WE DON'T KNOW THE FULL STORY, MAJOR, BUT AT POSITION FOUR REFERENCE SIXTEEN THE CRUSTAVONS MUST HAVE SOME KINDA BASE. WE'VE GOTTA GET THERE FAST!

STINGRAY

STRANGE undersea creatures known as Crustavons launch a missile from their surface base in the Brazilian jungle. The rocket's target is Washington.

STINGRAY, IN THE ARMY'S JUNGLE CAT, RACES TO THE AREA.

THE JUNGLE-CAT BREAKS INTO A CLEARING...

LOOK! THAT'S IT... THE BASE!

AT THAT MOMENT ANOTHER MISSILE IS FIRED.

BUT BEFORE THE CRUSTAVONS CAN PRESS THE FIRING BUTTON...

... THE JUNGLE CAT SENDS A HAIL OF ROCKETS INTO THE BASE.

SECONDS LATER...

WELL DONE, MAJOR... NOW IF YOU'LL DROP STINGRAY OFF AT THE COAST, WE'LL HEAD FOR HOME.

HALF AN HOUR LATER...

SO-LONG, MAJOR... AND THANKS!

SOON STINGRAY IS SPEEDING BACK TO THE UNITED STATES.

MISSILE HAS BEEN LAUNCHED FROM BASE TWO MILES AHEAD.

MARINA INDICATED THAT WASHINGTON WAS THE NEXT CITY TO BE ATTACKED.

YES, PHONES... WE'VE GOTTA WARN THEM.

TROY RADIOS TO COMMANDER SHORE AT MARINEVILLE...

OKAY, TROY...ALL TRACKING STATIONS HAVE BEEN ALERTED. FIND THAT BASE AND DESTROY IT!

DESTROY THAT MISSILE!

BENEATH THE GROUND, THE CRUSTAVONS BECOME AWARE OF THE DANGER...

STANDBY WITH DEFENCE ROCKETS...

WE'D BETTER MOVE CLEAR... BEFORE WE'RE CAUGHT IN THE BLAST.

FULL SPEED ASTERN... RAPID CRAWL!

TROY MAKES HIS ROUTINE CALL TO MARINEVILLE...

MISSION ENDED, COMMANDER.

GREAT, TROY...WE LOCATED AND INTERCEPTED THAT MISSILE HEADING FOR WASHINGTON. GUESS ATLANTA WILL FIX US A CELEBRATION MEAL WHEN SHE GETS BACK FROM THE BEACH.

BUT ON THE ISLE OF LEMOY...

SO, THE COMMANDER'S DAUGHTER IS ALONE ON THE BEACH. SHE IS JUST THE BAIT TITAN NEEDS TO CAPTURE TROY TEMPEST!

The house of Lemoy, secret headquarters of surface agent X20.

THE M[...] BE CHA[...] IT W[...]

BRING HER TO ME. SHE WILL BE BAIT TO CATCH TROY TEMPEST. I WILL DESTROY HIM ONCE AND FOR ALL!

X20 OPERATES ANOTHER CONTROL AND AN ELEVATOR RISES INTO THE ROOM...

SWIFTLY TITAN'S AGENT IS TAKEN DOWN TO THE CAVERN BENEATH THE HOUSE...

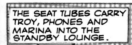

THE SEAT TUBES CARRY TROY, PHONES AND MARINA INTO THE STANDBY LOUNGE.

LET'S REPORT TO THE CONTROL TOWER...

COMMANDER SHORE IS ON DUTY...

HI, TROY... ATL[...] SHOULD BE H[...] BY NOW...

AT THAT MOMENT, TROY IS IN STINGRAY CHECKING HIS LOGS...

OKAY, PHONES...THAT'S IT, WE'VE FINISHED THE REPORT ON THAT BRAZILIAN AFFAIR...

YES, TROY...

HEH! HEH! THIS WILL BE EASY. ATLANTA WILL SUSPECT NOTHING... UNTIL IT IS TOO LATE!

X20 HEADS TOWARDS THE BEACH...

GOSH! LOOK AT THE TIME! TROY WILL BE BACK. OH, WHAT A PITY I WASN'T THERE TO MEET HIM!

...TERIOR OF THE HOUSE CAN ... PUSH OF A BUTTON...

...OKE

LEMOY'S SECRETS ARE UNCOVERED...

THE GIANT SCREEN ILLUMINATES. MIGHTY TITAN FILLS THE WALL.

WHAT HAVE YOU TO REPORT?

I HAVE LEARNED, YOUR MAJESTY, THAT ATLANTA, COMMANDER SHORE'S BEAUTIFUL DAUGHTER, IS ALONE ON THE BEACH.

A BOULDER IS MOVED AND PART OF THE CAVERN WALL SLIDES BACK...

THE MOTORS FIRE AND THE SMALL CRAFT RISES, HOVERING ABOVE GROUND... THEN IT MOVES TOWARDS THE CAVE MOUTH, AND INTO THE OCEAN...

BUT TROY GETS NO ANSWER...

...WE'LL ...YOUR ...SEE.

GUESS SHE'S STILL ON THE BEACH, PHONES.

LOOKS THAT WAY, TROY.

TITAN'S AGENT BEACHES HIS CRAFT BEHIND A ROCK...

NOW IS MY CHANCE!

Titan plans the destruction of Troy Tempest. He sends Surface Agent X20 to capture Atlanta.

DO NOT STRUGGLE, MY DEAR... THE MIGHTY TITAN WISHES TO SEE YOU.

HELPLESS, ATLANTA IS TAKEN TO X20'S BEACHED CRAFT.

THEN TROY NOTICES THE OMINOUS TRACKS...

PARKING BY ATLANTA'S CAR, TROY EXAMINES THE BEACH...

ATLANTA... WHERE ARE YOU, HONEY?

YOU'RE RIGHT, PHONES... TITAN WANTS YOU DEAD, TEMPEST. WATCH YOUR STEP... AND GOOD LUCK!

IT IS DECIDED NOT TO ENDANGER MARINA'S LIFE. TROY AND PHONES FLASH DOWN THE INJECTION TUBES...

ATLANTA IS BROUGHT BEFORE TITAN...

SO, YOU ARE ATLANTA... YES, TEMPEST WILL CERTAINLY ATTEMPT TO RESCUE YOU!

AND WHEN HE GETS HERE YOU'LL BE SORRY, FISH-HEAD!

TAKE HER TO THE ISLAND! WHEN WE HAVE SLAIN TEMPEST, SHE WILL DIE FOR THAT INSULT!

A TRAVEL TUBE CAR WHISKS ACROSS THE UNDERSEA CITY...

AT THAT MOMENT, TROY TEMPEST IS OUTSIDE THE SHORE RESIDENCE...

HELLO, COMMANDER... ATLANTA DOESN'T SEEM TO BE HOME.

MAYBE SHE'S STILL AT THE BEACH, TROY.

TROY RADIOS MARINEVILLE...

I'M SORRY, SIR, BUT I FIGURE ATLANTA'S BEEN KIDNAPPED BY ONE OF THE UNDERSEA ALIENS...

GET BACK HERE FAST, TEMPEST...I'VE HEARD FROM TITAN!

I GUESS SO... I'LL DRIVE OUT AND MEET HER.

TROY'S NEW ULTRA-POWERED HOVERCAR SCREAMS AWAY FROM MARINEVILLE...

THE TWENTY MILES THAT SEPERATE MARINEVILLE FROM THE BEACH ARE COVERED IN FOUR MINUTES...

THAT SHARK'S GOT MY DAUGHTER, CAPTAIN... SHE'S ON HER WAY TO TITANICA NOW.

RIGHT, SIR... I'LL GET AFTER HER AT ONCE.

THAT COULD BE TITAN'S ANGLE, TROY...

X20'S CRAFT APPROACHES TITANICA...

THE TERROR FISH STARTS ITS JOURNEY...

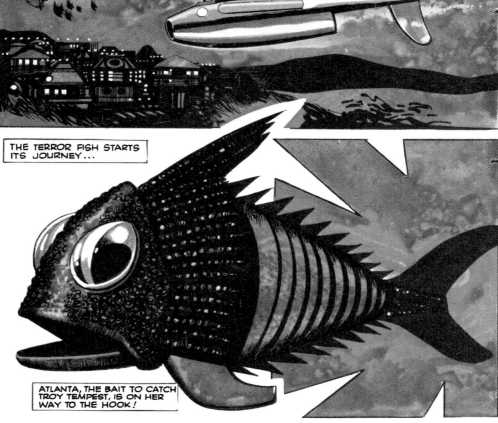

ATLANTA, THE BAIT TO CATCH TROY TEMPEST, IS ON HER WAY TO THE HOOK!

STINGRAY

To trap and destroy Troy Tempest, Titan has captured Atlanta and has ordered her to be taken by Terror Fish to a mysterious island.

MEANWHILE, STINGRAY SPEEDS TOWARDS TITANICA...

TITAN'S TOO PROUD TO KILL ME OUTRIGHT... HE'LL WANT TO PROLONG THE AGONY. I DON'T WANT ANY ARGUMENTS, PHONES... WE'LL DO THIS MY WAY.

OKAY, TROY... BUT I DON'T HAVE TO LIKE IT! THERE'S TITANICA UP AHEAD...

THE EVIL ABODE OF TITAN...

TROY LEAVES STINGRAY...

BUT TITAN'S MINIONS HAVE OTHER IDEAS...

THE STRANGE LIQUID ENVELOPES TROY...

TROY'S FOCUS BECOMES CLEARER AND WHAT HE SEES MAKES HIS PULSE RACE...

HIS SE
RESIST
AS HE

SO YOU HAVE RECOVERED, TEMPEST. TAKE HIM TO THE ISLAND. IT IS TIME FOR HIM TO DIE!

STINGRAY

Phones, in Stingray, prepares to attack a Titan Terror Fish, not knowing that Troy is aboard . . .

PHONES SLOWS STINGRAY, PLANNING TO FOLLOW AT A SAFE DISTANCE...

GALUB BABLUBBLE HOIGHT A CARUBBLE?

CONLUBBA SLUBBA... NACHT! HUBBLER!!

AN AQUAPHIBIAN HAND MOVES ON TO A CONTROL...

THEN...

THE ON. CUT

WHY YOU... IF PHONES IS HURT I'LL KILL YOU...SOMEHOW I'LL GET YOU!

THE WAVES ON THE LAGOON DIE TO A RIPPLE AS THE TERROR FISH DIVES... AND TROY GETS UNSTEADILY TO HIS FEET...

HE CRASHES ON TO THE HARD ROUGH CORAL BANK.

WHAT ARE THEY UP TO? THEY'VE UNTIED ME...AND THE TERROR FISH IS SUBMERGING... I DON'T GET IT! THEY'VE EVEN LEFT ME A KNIFE...

A CORAL AROUND A S LAKE...BUT THEY LEFT GUESS I'M N

STINGRAY

Atlanta has been captured by Titan. Troy Tempest falls for the evil undersea tyrant's trap and after seeing Stingray hit by a Terror Fish missile, he is taken to a coral island. Then he sees Atlanta staked out on an outcrop which is separated from him by an expanse of salt water . . .

HOLD ON, ATLANTA... I'M GONNA SWIM ACROSS.

STILL PUZZLED AS TO THE R RELEASE FROM HIS BONDS

TROY... BEHIND YOU!

SO THAT'S TITAN'S GAME! I SHOULD HAVE REALISED IT WAS TOO EASY!

THE VICIOUS MAN-KILLER STREAKS AFTER ITS PREY...

THE SHARK LUNGES...TROY WHIPS HIS BODY TO ONE SIDE...

MEANWHILE, ON THE OCEAN BED CLOSE TO TITANICA...

BRUISED AND SHAKEN AFTER THE TERROR FISH ATTACK, PHONES SWIMS OUT TO EXAMINE STINGRAY...

HMMM... HAVE TO SEAL THE EQUIPMENT BAY...BUT I RECKON SHE'LL BE OKAY. I'VE GOTTA GET MOVING AND TRY TO FIND WHERE THEY TOOK TROY!

SLOWLY AT FIRST, AND THEN ALMOST RECKLESSLY, PHONES CHECKS OUT STINGRAY'S MOTORS...

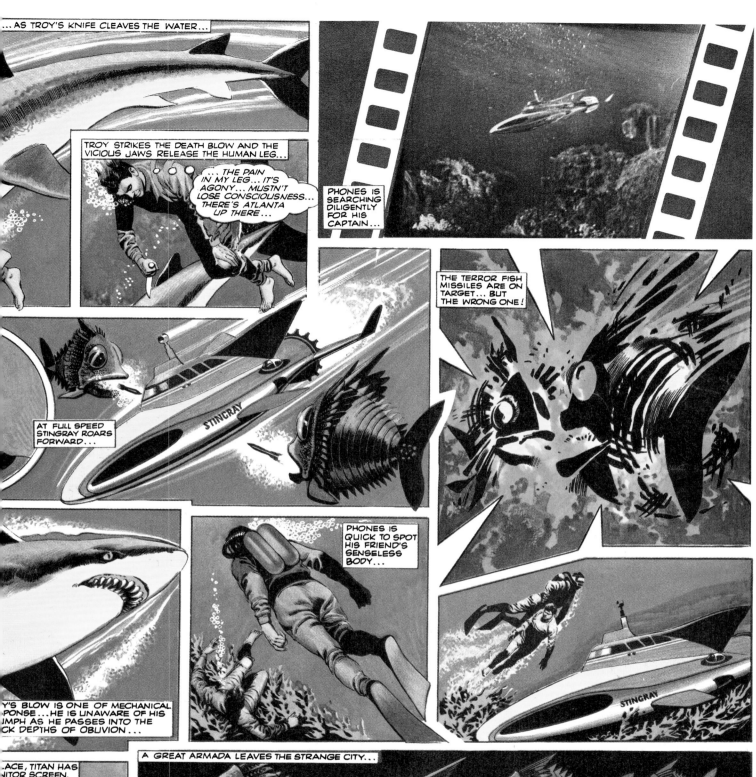

...AS TROY'S KNIFE CLEAVES THE WATER...

TROY STRIKES THE DEATH BLOW AND THE VICIOUS JAWS RELEASE THE HUMAN LEG...

...THE PAIN IN MY LEG...IT'S AGONY... MUSTN'T LOSE CONSCIOUSNESS... THERE'S ATLANTA UP THERE...

PHONES IS SEARCHING DILIGENTLY FOR HIS CAPTAIN...

AT FULL SPEED STINGRAY ROARS FORWARD...

THE TERROR FISH MISSILES ARE ON TARGET... BUT THE WRONG ONE!

PHONES IS QUICK TO SPOT HIS FRIEND'S SENSELESS BODY...

...Y'S BLOW IS ONE OF MECHANICAL ...PONSE...HE IS UNAWARE OF HIS ...IMPH AS HE PASSES INTO THE ...CK DEPTHS OF OBLIVION...

...ACE, TITAN HAS ...NITOR SCREEN.

...I SQUADRONS ...ENTY SEVEN...LAUNCH ...ESTROY THEM ALL!

A GREAT ARMADA LEAVES THE STRANGE CITY...

45

STINGRAY

After an almost fatal fight in a shark infested lake, Troy Tempest is taken aboard Stingray, and Atlanta, put up by Titan as bait to catch Troy, is rescued from danger. But Titan, seeing his schemes going wrong, sends an armada of terror fish to destroy Tempest and his friends . . .

STINGRAY DOWN TO THE TUNN THAT LEA THROUGH CORAL FR THE OCE

TROY'S MIND IS MADE UP. HE HOBBLES TO THE CONTROLS.

WE'LL HAVE TO BLAST OUR WAY OUT, PHONES...ACCELERATION RATE SIX... STAND BY STING MISSILES!

STANDING BY!

STINGRAY BURSTS INTO THE OCEAN...

FIRE!!

GOOD THING THOSE AQUAPHIBIANS DON'T KNOW THAT!

NOW COME ON, TROY... BACK TO THE COUCH AND REST. CAN WE GO HOME, PHONES, TROY NEEDS A DOCTOR.

PHONES NODS AND TURNS STINGRAY TO THE HOMEWARD COURSE...

PICKING UP SOUNDSCAN SIGNALS, TROY... MUST BE TWENTY OR MORE TERROR FISH AT THE END OF THAT TUNNEL.

I'M COMING UP FRONT, PHONES. MOVE OVER.

NO, TROY... YOUR LEG... YOU SHOULD REST.

THE SUPERIOR FIRE POWER OF STINGRAY IS UNLEASHED...

... AND EVENTUALLY TRIUMPHS.

SHALL WE LET 'EM GO, TROY...?

YES, PHONES... GUESS WE'RE OUT OF STING MISSILES ANYHOW.

LATER...

MAY I HAVE THIS AFTERNOON OFF, FATHER? TROY LEAVES HOSPITAL TODAY.

I KNOW, ATLANTA... AND YOU WANT TO ARRANGE A LITTLE SURPRISE. OKAY, HONEY... OFF YOU GO.

TROY ARRIVES AT THE SHORE HOME, HIS LEG NEARLY HEALED...

ANY FRESH NEWS ON THE KAPLAN'S ASSASSINATION, COMMANDER?

NOT YET, TROY — COLONEL ZODIAC'S STILL ON THE CASE... AND MAKING PROGRESS, I HEAR!

OH, DON'T SPOIL OUR DINNER WITH TALK OF DANGER AND DUTY... MY GUESS IS WE'LL GET PLENTY OF THAT IN THE FUTURE. LET'S LEAVE IT UNTIL THEN.

THE END

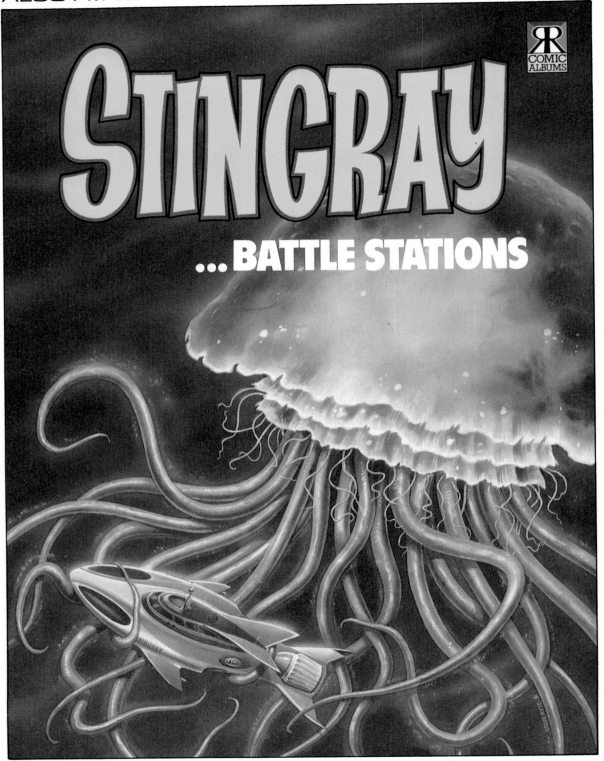